Contents

Answers to the questions are on the back of the pull-out Poster in the middle of the book.

Published by Coordination Group Publications Ltd.

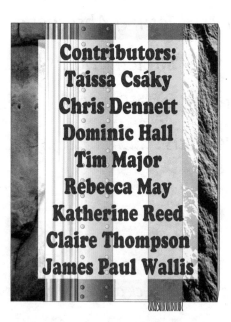

Contributors:
Taissa Csáky
Chris Dennett
Dominic Hall
Tim Major
Rebecca May
Katherine Reed
Claire Thompson
James Paul Wallis

ISBN 1-84146-254-3

Groovy website: www.cgpbooks.co.uk
Jolly bits of clipart from CorelDRAW
Printed by Elanders Hindson, Newcastle upon Tyne.

With thanks to Christine Tinkler and Glenn Rogers for the proof-reading.

Background

Materials are the stuff that objects are made of.
You may already know some of them — like wood, plastic and metal.

Q1   These pictures show materials. Choose **two** descriptions from the blue blob to match each material and write them down. You can use descriptions more than once.

WOOD

not see-through
....
....

PLASTIC

....
....

GLASS

....
....

absorbent (soaks up water)   see-through   flexible (bendy)
waterproof   strong   hard
not waterproof   easily broken   not see-through   soft   stiff

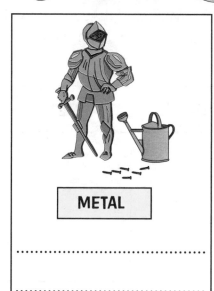

METAL

....
....

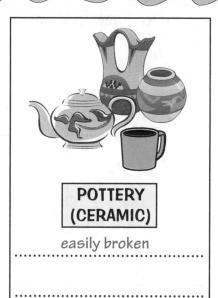

POTTERY (CERAMIC)

easily broken
....
....

FABRIC (CLOTH)

....
....

Material — it's just, you know, stuff...

In science, material isn't just the stuff your clothes are made of — that is fabric.
This book is about different materials and what they are like.

2

Materials are Used for Different Things

Different objects can be made from the same material.
You can find everyday materials like wood, glass, plastic and metal everywhere.

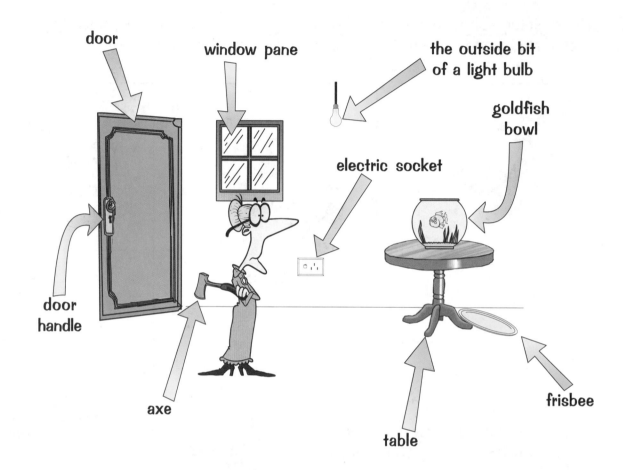

door

window pane

the outside bit
of a light bulb

goldfish
bowl

electric socket

door
handle

axe

frisbee

table

Q1 In this picture, the arrows point to things made of WOOD, METAL, GLASS or PLASTIC.
Fill in the table to show what things from the picture are made out of each material.

GLASS	WOOD	PLASTIC	METAL
1. *the outside bit of a light bulb*	1.	1.	1.
2.	2.	2.	2.
3.			

'Cos we are living in a material world...

One material can be made into lots of different objects. Just think of how many
things you can make out of plastic — dog bowls, buckets, jelly moulds...

© CGP 2002

How to Recognise Materials

This page is about recognising materials. Looking at them is a good start.

Q1   Look around the room you are sitting in now. Find **two** things made of
each material and **write them below**. Then write **two descriptions** from
the orange blob to show how you recognised the material.

> TWO OBJECTS MADE OF
> THIS MATERIAL ARE...

> I COULD TELL, BECAUSE
> THEY WERE...

WOOD

....
....

....
....

GLASS

....
....

....
....

*Glass can be very sharp
— don't cut yourself.*

METAL

....
....

....
....

PLASTIC

....
....

....
....

strong   see-through   not see-through

soft

waterproof   absorbent (soaks up water)

easily broken   wood-grain patterned   shiny

brightly coloured   flexible (bendy)   hard

> The wood didn't want
> to be recognised.

... and I am a material girl...

It's hard to tell what material some objects are made from.
Plastic sometimes has a wood-grain pattern to make it look nicer. Don't be fooled!

Material Properties

Different materials have different properties.
Some are hard, some are soft, some are strong, some are... well, you get the idea.

Q1 Fill in this table about materials and their properties.
You'll need to find the materials, and have a look at them.
Say what the material is **usually** like. I've done some for you.

Material	Property				
	Hard or soft?	Strong or weak?	Stiff or flexible?	Transparent or not transparent?	Rough or smooth?
metal	hard				
wood				Not transparent	
glass					
rubber			Flexible		
plastic					
wool					
cotton					
ceramic					

So do you get hammers made from wool?...

Remember, '_properties_ of materials' means what things are _like_.
Sometimes people say '_characteristics_ of materials' instead — it means the same thing.

Guess the Material

See if you can guess which materials I'm talking about...

Q1　Read these descriptions of materials. For each one, tick (✓) one of the boxes to say which material it is more likely to be.

a) I am usually **hard** and **strong**. What am I?

wood ☐　　　wool ☐

b) I am usually **soft** and **flexible**. What am I?

glass ☐　　　rubber ☐

The aliens have no idea what it is. Maybe they should read the label...

c) I am usually **stiff** and **smooth**. What am I?

ceramic ☐　　　rubber ☐　　　cotton ☐

d) I am usually **strong** and **flexible**. What am I?

plastic ☐　　　glass ☐

e) I am usually **hard**, **weak** and **stiff**. What am I?

metal ☐　　　wood ☐　　　glass ☐

I am brown and sticky, what am I?...*

Did you know, the hardest thing in the world is a diamond. They put tiny diamonds on the edges of saws and drills to stop them wearing down. Diamonds are also quite pretty!

*A stick.　　　© CGP 2002

6

Comparing Materials

When you know about the properties of materials, you can work out
which materials are harder / softer / smoother than others...

Q1   For each pair, tick (✓) the box to show which material is usually **softer**.

a) metal ☐ ☐ paper

Remember — the softer something is, the easier it is to scratch.

c) ceramic ☐ ☐ plastic

b) wood ☐ ☐ rubber

d) glass ☐ ☐ wool

Q2   Which of these is usually **strongest**? Write the name of the **strongest** material.

wool   paper   metal   plastic   ....

Q3   Sputnik the alien wants to stand on the **most flexible** material. Work out which
of these is usually the **most flexible**, and draw Sputnik standing on top of it.

Sputnik

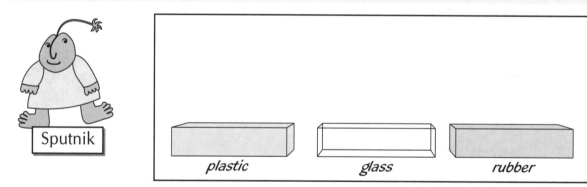

plastic   *glass*   *rubber*

Q4   Tick (✓) the boxes to complete this table comparing wood and glass.

I've done the first column for you.

	hardest	easiest to break	roughest	most see-through
wood	✓			
glass				

I am green and sticky, what am I?...*

One way to tell whether a material is harder than another, is to rub them together — the softer one
will get scratched. But always ask the person who owns them first, you could ruin them!

*A mouldy stick.

Same Material — Different Forms

Different objects made from the same material can be different.
A wooden spoon is rough, but a wooden table is smooth.

Q1 a) Is wood usually **strong** or **weak**?
Write 'strong' or 'weak'.   ....

b) Here are two different things made of wood. Which is **strong**, and which is **weak**?
Write 'strong' or 'weak' next to the pictures.

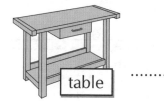 table   ....    match   ....

Q2 a) Is metal usually **stiff** or **flexible** (bendy)?
Write 'stiff' or 'flexible'.   ....

b) These things are both made of metal. Which is **stiff**, and which is **flexible**?
Write 'stiff' or 'flexible' next to the pictures.

 foil   ....    girder   ....

Q3 a) Is rock usually **rough** or **smooth**?
Write 'rough' or 'smooth'.   ....

b) These things are made of rock. Are they **rough** or **smooth**?
Write 'rough' or 'smooth' next to the pictures.

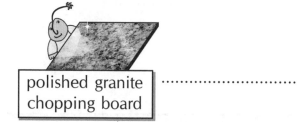 polished granite chopping board   ....    granite cliff   ....

I am orange and sticky, what am I?...*

The most important thing to remember is what materials are <u>usually</u> like.

*An orange sticker.

Using Materials

The properties of a material make it good for some things and bad for others.
For example — glass makes a good window, but a bad football.

Q1 The properties in the green box belong to cotton or metal. Write the property that belongs to cotton in the cotton box and write the property of metal in the metal box.

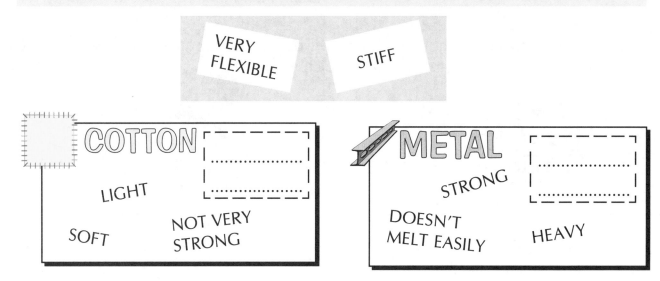

VERY FLEXIBLE

STIFF

COTTON

LIGHT

SOFT

NOT VERY STRONG

METAL

STRONG

DOESN'T MELT EASILY

HEAVY

Q2 Pick one property from the cotton box that makes cotton good for making clothes. Write down the property you've chosen and say why it's good.

Property = ...

This property is good for making clothes because: ....

....

Q3 Which two properties of metal make it a bad material for making clothes? Choose properties from the metal box for your answer.

1. ....

2. ....

Bad idea number 98 — inflatable pincushion...

Metal is a good material to use for making cars, but it's bad for clothes (unless you are the tin man). Cotton is good for making clothes, but terrible for making cars.

Using Materials

A page full of materials, properties and uses — get stuck in...

Q1   Fill in the table at the bottom to show good and bad materials for making things.
Use the boxes of properties on this page and page 8. I've done the first one for you.

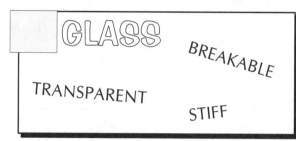

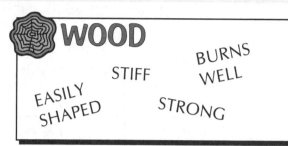

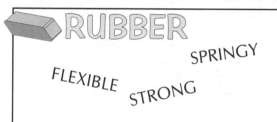

Silk is also very, very smooth. Some ties are made of silk. If you see one in a shop, pick it up and feel how smooth the silk is.

Object	Good material	One property that makes it good.	Bad material	One property that makes it bad.
PARACHUTE	silk	very light	metal	heavy
FISH TANK				
TABLE				
BARBECUE				
NAIL				

My rubber duck is made of plastic!...

For something to work properly it needs to be made of the right material.
If something is made of the wrong material it won't work properly — like a lead balloon!

Choosing the Right Material

This page is about Bob — well, Bob and designing stuff.
Designing means thinking about how to make something and which material to use.

Q1 Bob is designing a crash helmet. He's trying to find the best material to use.
He asked three questions about each material and he put the results in a table.

Material	What colours does it come in?	How heavy is it?	How safe is it?
Material 1	black	very heavy	very safe
Material 2	green & red	light	safe
Material 3	black & white	heavy	safe
Material 4	blue & yellow	very heavy	not safe at all
Material 5	grey	very light	very safe
Material 6	red, blue & grey	heavy	not safe at all

a) Which is the **most** important property for a crash helmet? (Circle) the best answer.

The colours it comes in.   How heavy it is.   How safe it is.

b) Which is the **least** important property for a crash helmet?
(Circle) the best answer.

The colours it comes in.   How heavy it is.   How safe it is.

c) What is the best material for Bob
to use for the crash helmet?   ....

Mike's helmet was safe, but the colour was all wrong.

d) Why is this the best material to use?

....

....

Good design — barbed wire fence...

Choosing the right material is very important when you design things. You have to look
for materials with the properties you need. Then you have to choose the best one.

Choosing the Right Material

As the title says, this page is all about choosing the right material... simple as that.

Q1　What is the most important property to look for if you are making welly boots?
Put a tick (✓) next to the correct answer.

How waterproof the material is. ☐

What colour the material is. ☐

How shiny the material is. ☐

Q2　On a trip to the planet Zargle, Sue found a wonderful new material called "Biff".
Biff has loads of good properties that are written below.

PROPERTIES		
	stronger than steel	sucks up bad smells
heavy	fireproof	slippery

a)　What property of Biff makes it good for making a bridge?

....

b)　Why is Biff a bad material to use to make goalkeeping gloves?

....

c)　What **two** properties make Biff a good material to use for making a fireman's helmet?

1...　　　2...

Bad design — barbed wire underpants...

A material has lots of different properties. So it can be good for making lots of things.
Wood is easily shaped and it burns well — so it's good for making chairs or for burning.

Investigating Properties of Materials

You can test a material to see if it has a certain property.
You need to do different tests to find out about different properties.

Q1 Each of these pictures shows a different test. Match the descriptions to
the pictures — then write the correct description next to each picture.

*A test to see
if a material is
elastic (stretchy).*

*A test to see
if a material
soaks up liquid.*

*A test to see if a
material is transparent
(see-through).*

*A test to see
if a material
can be worn away.*

....

....

....

....

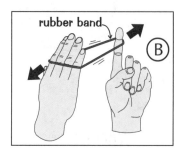

....

....

....

....

I did a test to see if my house would float...

You can test for any property of materials, but some properties are easier to spot than
others. Understand the tricky ones now and the whole book will be much easier.

KS2 Answers — Characteristics of Materials

Page 16 Testing Absorbency

Q1: 1. Cut the pieces of paper to the same size.
2. Leave each piece in the water for the same length of time.

Page 17 Testing Absorbency

Q1: kitchen roll

Q2: tracing paper and exercise book paper

Q3: Doctor Peanut did not *MEASURE* the amount of water left after each test.
She *CAN'T* tell if tracing paper is more absorbent than exercise book paper.
And she can't tell if sugar paper is better than *PAPER TOWEL*.
She *SHOULD* have measured the amount of water left. Then she would
KNOW how much water was soaked up by each piece of paper.

Page 18 Testing Absorbency

Results will depend on your experiment — I've used the spare results.

TYPE OF PAPER	WATER LEFT (in ml)
Paper towel	15 ml
Kitchen roll	10 ml
Tracing paper	24 ml
Sugar paper	20 ml
Tissue	12 ml

Page 19 Testing Absorbency

Q1: The one that left behind the least water is the most absorbent.

Q2: Results will depend on your experiment — I've used the spare results.

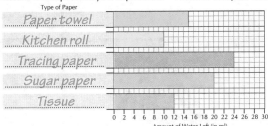

Type of Paper: Paper towel, Kitchen roll, Tracing paper, Sugar paper, Tissue
Amount of Water Left (in ml): 0 2 4 6 8 10 12 14 16 18 20 22 24 26 28 30

Q3: Results will depend on your experiment — I've used the spare results.
1. Kitchen roll — Most absorbent
2. Tissue
3. Paper towel
4. Sugar paper
5. Tracing paper — Least absorbent

Page 20 Stretchy Tights

Q1: Always measure from the waist to the toe.
Use the same ball to test each pair of tights.
Wait for the ball to stop swinging before you measure the length.

Page 21 Stretchy Tights

Q1: Results will depend on your experiment — I've used the spare results.
Tennis ball

Q2: Results will depend on your experiment — I've used the spare results.

Pair	Length BEFORE stretching	Length AFTER stretching	How much did the tights stretch?
A	91 cm	120 cm	29 cm
B	88 cm	105 cm	17 cm
C	95 cm	122 cm	27 cm
D	90 cm	114 cm	24 cm

Q3: Results will depend on your experiment — I've used the spare results.

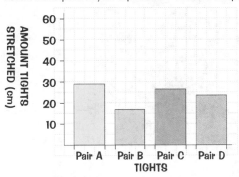

AMOUNT TIGHTS STRETCHED (cm): 10 20 30 40 50 60
TIGHTS: Pair A, Pair B, Pair C, Pair D

Q4: Results will depend on your experiment — I've used the spare results.
The MOST STRETCHY tights were PAIR A.
The LEAST STRETCHY tights were PAIR B.

Page 22 Testing Materials for a Purpose

Q1: It needs to float on water.
It needs to be waterproof.

Q2: umbrella fabric, pottery plate, raincoat fabric

Q3: Put water on to the materials to see if they let it pass through.

Page 23 Testing Materials for a Purpose

Q1: Put the armchair in water to see if it floats or sinks.

Q2: The armchairs should all be the same size.
The armchairs should all be the same shape.

Q3: When you test for the *PROPERTIES* of a material it's best to compare them
with *LOTS OF* other materials. Materials usually need to have *MORE THAN*
one useful property.

Page 24 Revision Questions

Q1: These are suggested answers — they will vary depending on what form
of the material you're thinking of.

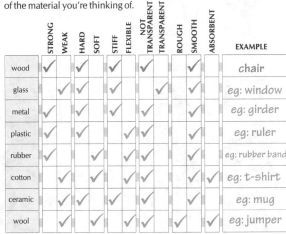

	STRONG	WEAK	HARD	SOFT	STIFF	FLEXIBLE	NOT TRANSPARENT	TRANSPARENT	ROUGH	SMOOTH	ABSORBENT	EXAMPLE
wood	✓		✓		✓		✓			✓		chair
glass		✓	✓		✓			✓		✓		eg: window
metal	✓		✓		✓		✓			✓		eg: girder
plastic	✓				✓	✓				✓		eg: ruler
rubber	✓					✓				✓		eg: rubber band
cotton		✓		✓		✓				✓	✓	eg: t-shirt
ceramic			✓		✓		✓			✓		eg: mug
wool		✓		✓		✓			✓		✓	eg: jumper

Q2: plastic bag: WEAK
plastic slide: STRONG

Page 25 Revision Questions

Q1: Suggested answers:
window: GLASS, because it's HARD, STIFF and TRANSPARENT.
pin: METAL, because it's STRONG, HARD, STIFF and SMOOTH.

Q2: To test an object's *HARDNESS* we tried scratching it with a penknife.
To test an object's *FLEXIBILITY* we measured how far we could bend it.

Q3: Only change the thing you're testing and keep everything else the same.

Chocolate

POUR HOT WATER INTO THE TEAPOT... ... AND WAIT 5 MINUTES...

A BAD material

CHOCOLATE IS STIFF
... WHEN IT'S COLD — SO IT KEEPS ITS SHAPE WHEN COLD

BUT...
IT MELTS VERY EASILY
... SO IT CAN'T HOLD HOT WATER

IT'S WATERPROOF
... SO IT CAN HOLD WATER

KS2 Answers — Characteristics of Materials

Page 1 Background

Q1: These are suggested answers — answers may vary depending on what form of the material you're thinking of. E.g. answers for plastic could vary a lot.
WOOD — not see-through (given)
        plus any 1 of: waterproof, strong, hard, stiff
PLASTIC — any 2 of: waterproof, strong, not see-through, hard, flexible (bendy)
GLASS — any 2 of: waterproof, easily broken, see-through, hard, stiff
METAL — any 2 of: waterproof, strong, not see-through, hard, stiff
POTTERY — easily broken (given)
        plus any 1 of: waterproof, not see-through, hard, stiff
FABRIC — any 2 of: not waterproof, absorbent, strong, not see-through, soft, flexible (bendy)

Page 2 Materials are Used for Different Things

Q1: GLASS — 1. the outside bit of a light bulb (given)
                2. window pane 3. goldfish bowl
WOOD — 1. door 2. table
PLASTIC — 1. electric socket 2. frisbee
METAL — 1. door handle 2. axe

Page 3 How to Recognise Materials

Q1: There are various answers for this question — main thing to check is that the properties match the object chosen.

Page 4 Material Properties

Q1: Answers will depend on what form of the material you're thinking of.

Material	Property				
	Hard or soft?	Strong or weak?	Stiff or flexible?	Transparent or not transparent?	Rough or smooth?
metal	hard	strong	stiff	Not transparent	smooth
wood	hard	strong	stiff	Not transparent	smooth
glass	hard	weak	stiff	Transparent	smooth
rubber	soft	strong	flexible	Not transparent	smooth
plastic	hard	strong	flexible	Not transparent	smooth
wool	soft	weak	flexible	Not transparent	rough
cotton	soft	weak	flexible	Not transparent	smooth
ceramic	hard	weak	stiff	Not transparent	smooth

Page 5 Guess the Material

Q1: a) wood b) rubber c) ceramic d) plastic e) glass

Page 6 Comparing Materials

Q1: a) paper b) rubber c) plastic d) wool
Q2: metal
Q3:

plastic   glass   rubber

NB Plastic is usually flexible, but usually not as flexible as rubber.

Q4:

	hardest	easiest to break	roughest	most see-through
wood	✓		✓	
glass		✓		✓

Page 7 Same Material — Different Forms

Q1: a) strong b) table: strong; match: weak
Q2: a) stiff b) foil: flexible; girder: stiff
Q3: a) rough b) chopping board: smooth; cliff: rough

Page 8 Using Materials

Q1: Cotton: very flexible, Metal: stiff
Q2: Property — accept any of: soft, very flexible, light.
       Accept any reason as long as it matches property.
Q3: heavy, stiff

Page 9 Using Materials

Q1: These are some possible answers — answers will vary.

Object	Good material	What property makes it good?	Bad material	What property makes it bad?
PARACHUTE	silk	very light	metal	heavy
FISH TANK	glass	transparent	rubber	bendy
TABLE	wood	stiff	cotton	not very strong
BARBECUE	metal	doesn't melt easily	wood	burns well
NAIL	metal	not flexible	glass	breakable

Page 10 Choosing the Right Material

Q1: a) How safe it is.
       b) The colours it comes in.
       c) Material 5
       d) It's very safe and it's very light.
          (The other very safe material is Material 1, but that's very heavy.)

Page 11 Choosing the Right Material

Q1: How waterproof the material is.
Q2: a) stronger than steel b) slippery c) 1. fireproof 2. stronger than steel

Page 12 Investigating Properties of Materials

Q1: A: A test to see if a material soaks up liquid.
       B: A test to see if a material is elastic (stretchy).
       C: A test to see if a material can be worn away.
       D: A test to see if a material is transparent (see-through).

Page 13 Investigating Properties of Materials

Q1: Put the wood in deep water and see if it sinks or floats.
Q2: Prop up the ruler at both ends and put weights in the middle to see if it breaks.
Q3: Ned could put each PLANK on the ground and then he could DROP objects onto it. If the objects don't DENT the wood then it shows that it is a HARD material.
Q4: That type of wood wasn't hard.

Page 14 Fair Tests

Q1: Furio rubbed the rocks with DIFFERENT things each time. The steel file would probably wear away the rocks much MORE than the block of wood. That means that he DOESN'T know which rock is harder.
Q2: He may have rubbed harder on the grimstone than the dullite.
Q3: "He should use the same object to rub each rock."
       and "He should rub each rock exactly the same way."

Page 15 Fair Tests

Q1: Furio dropped the ball from a higher point the second time.
Q2: Any answer along the lines of:
       "He could drop the ball from the same height each time."
Q3: To do a fair test you should change ONE THING at a time. You should keep everything else THE SAME each time.

Investigating Properties of Materials

This page has more stuff about testing for properties of materials.
You have to decide what the best tests would be.

Q1 How could you test if a block of wood floats in water? (Circle) the good test.

Drip water onto the wood to see if it absorbs the water.

Put the wood in really shallow water so it can't sink.

Put the wood in deep water and see if it sinks or floats.

Q2 Ned wants to find out if his plastic ruler is made of **strong** material.
Which of these tests would give him the answer? Put a tick (✓) next to the right one.

☐ Try to scratch the ruler with something hard.

☐ Try to wear the plastic away by rubbing it.

Remember: strong materials hold weight without breaking.

☐ Prop up the ruler at both ends and put weights in the middle to see if it breaks.

Q3 Ned has some planks of wood. He wants to find out how **hard** the different types of wood are. Fill in the blanks to say **one** way he could find out.

PLANK DENT HARD DROP

Ned could put each .... on the ground and

then he could .... objects onto it.

If the objects don't .... the wood then it

shows that the wood is a .... material.

Q4 Ned did the investigation, and one plank got a huge dent in it.
Tick (✓) the right conclusion about the type of wood.

That type of wood was hard. ☐

That type of wood wasn't hard. ☐

Ned thought there was time for just one more hardness test.

I had to get a new house...

Some of this page is a bit nasty. Make sure you have sorted out the difference between <u>hardness</u> and <u>strength</u>. Loads of people get them mixed up, including me.

14

Fair Tests

If you do any test you need to make sure it's a <u>fair</u> test.
Otherwise your investigation may give you the wrong answers.

Furio wants to find out which of his two types of rock is **harder**.
The pictures below show how he did his investigation.

Furio rubbed a grimstone rock with a block of wood...

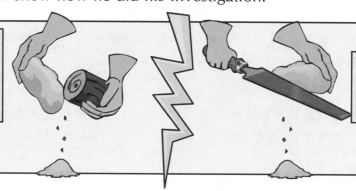

...then he rubbed a dullite rock with a steel file.

Q1 (Circle) the right words to describe the problems with his test.

Furio rubbed the rocks with (THE SAME / DIFFERENT) things each time. The steel

file would probably wear away the rocks much (MORE / LESS) than the block of

wood. That means that he (DOES / DOESN'T) know which rock is harder.

Q2 When Furio rubbed the grimstone he was full of energy — but when he rubbed the
dullite he was very tired. Why might that affect the test? (Circle) the right answer.

The dullite would be
softer if he was tired.

He may have rubbed harder on the
grimstone than the dullite.

Q3 How should Furio make his investigation a fair test?
Put a tick (✓) next to the **two** good answers.

He should use different objects to rub each rock. ☐

He should use the same object to rub each rock. ☐

He should rub one rock less than the other. ☐

He should rub each rock exactly the same way. ☐

Furio found some
rocks that he really
didn't want to rub.

Grimstones — meet the grimstones...

Fair tests are brilliant. Do tests fairly and you can be sure the results will make sense.
I really think that fair tests are the best thing ever — and so should you.

© CGP 2002

Fair Tests

Lucky you — an extra page on fair tests...
This is a different investigation — but the fair test rules are the same.

Furio has done another hardness test.
He dropped weights onto two **different** plastic tiles to see which one got deeper dents.

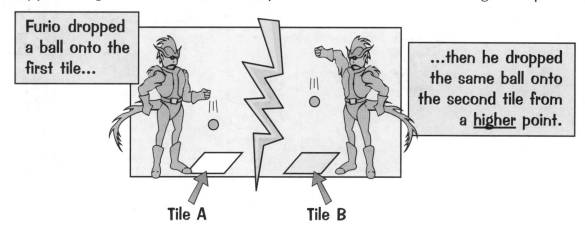

Furio dropped a ball onto the first tile...

...then he dropped the same ball onto the second tile from a <u>higher</u> point.

Tile A   **Tile B**

Q1 Look at the pictures and then put a tick (✓) next to the thing that made the test **unfair**.

☐ The ball was heavier the second time.

☐ Furio dropped the ball from a higher point the second time.

☐ Furio was more tired the second time.

Q2 How could Furio make the investigation a fair test?
Write your answer on the dotted lines. (Hint: use your answer to Q1.)

....

....

Q3 Fill in the gaps in these sentences about fair tests, using words from the box.

To do a fair test you should change

.... at a time.

You should keep everything else

.... each time.

THE SAME   DIFFERENT   ONE THING   LOTS OF THINGS

All the fun of the fair...

I reckon that after a while you'll do tests fairly — without even thinking about it.
Until then, you'd better keep practising fair tests again and again and again...

MINI-PROJECT 1

Testing Absorbency

Doctor Peanut wants to know what's best for mopping up liquids. She's doing an experiment to test the absorbency of different types of paper (how well each type soaks up water).

Equipment:

1. measuring cylinder

2. water

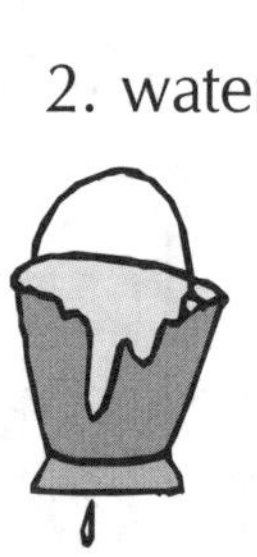

3. different types of paper

4. plastic tray

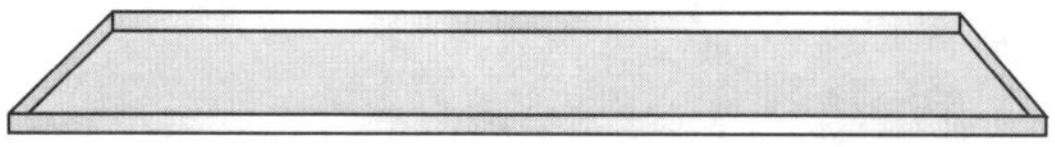

Experiment:

1. Cut out a piece of each type of paper.
2. Put the plastic tray on a desk.
3. For each piece of paper:
   – measure 25 ml of water and pour it onto the plastic tray,
   – put the piece of paper over the pool of water,
   – wait a while, then look at the amount of water left,
   – write the results in a table.

Q1 Write down **two ways** to make this a **fair test**. Choose from the list, then write your answers below.

Cut the pieces of paper to the same size.

Cut the pieces of paper to different sizes.

Leave each piece in the water for the same length of time.

Guess the amount of water instead of measuring it.

Doctor Peanut got carried away with cutting the paper.

1. ....

2. ....

Mmm... soggy paper — nice...

I don't care if you are sick of hearing about fair testing. It's dead important, so do it.

Testing Absorbency

Doctor Peanut has done the experiment.
Here are her results:

TYPE OF PAPER	HOW MUCH WATER WAS LEFT?
kitchen roll	no water left
sugar paper	hardly any water left
tracing paper	almost all the water left
exercise book paper	almost all the water left
paper towel	hardly any water left

Q1 Which was the most absorbent type of paper? ....

Q2 Which were the least absorbent types of paper? ....

and

....

Q3 Doctor Peanut wants to put the pieces of paper in order of absorbency. Circle the right words to explain why she can't put them in order.

Doctor Peanut did not TREASURE / MEASURE the amount of water left after each test.

She CAN / CAN'T tell if tracing paper is more absorbent than exercise book paper.

And she can't tell if sugar paper is better than KITCHEN ROLL / PAPER TOWEL.

She SHOULD / SHOULDN'T have measured the amount of water left. Then she

would KNOW / GUESS how much water was soaked up by each piece of paper.

*What is an octopus? — an eight-sided cat...**

Measure <u>everything</u> — don't guess. That way you'll get much, much better results.

* This has nothing to do with the page. I just felt like telling a joke...

Testing Absorbency

This is where you do your own investigation.
The aim is to put five different types of paper in order of absorbency.

Equipment you'll need:

1. measuring cylinder
2. water
3. five different types of paper

(You don't have to use the same types as Doctor Peanut used.)

4. plastic tray
5. stopwatch

The investigation:

1. Cut out a 10 cm square piece of each type of paper.
2. Put the plastic tray on a desk.
3. For each piece of paper:
   – measure 30 ml of water and pour it into the plastic tray,
   – put the piece of paper over the pool of water,
   – time 30 seconds with the stopwatch then take the paper out,
   – pour the water left in the tray into the measuring cylinder,
   – write down the amount of water in the table below.

Your results*:

TYPE OF PAPER	WATER LEFT (in ml)
....	.... ml
....	.... ml
....	.... ml
....	.... ml
....	.... ml

REMEMBER: you need to <u>measure</u> the amount of water left — using the measuring cylinder.

Testing absorbency — a laugh a minute...

Always read the instructions before you start the investigation. You need to have your stopwatch ready so you can start timing as soon as the paper touches the water.

* If you can't do the experiment, you can use my spare results:
paper towel: 15 ml / kitchen roll: 10 ml / tracing paper: 24 ml / sugar paper: 20 ml / tissue: 12 ml

Testing Absorbency

The point of an investigation is to find something out.
You should always look at your results afterwards — to see what you've found out.

Q1 How can you tell which paper is the most absorbent? Tick (✓) the right answer.

☐ *The one that left behind the most water is the most absorbent.*

☐ *The one that left behind the least water is the most absorbent.*

Q2 Draw a bar chart of your results.

Write the name of the paper on the left. Draw a bar going across for each one — to say how much water was left.

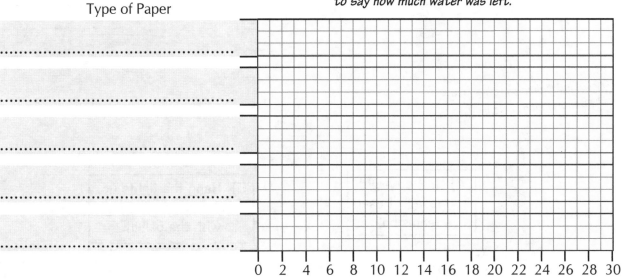

Type of Paper

....

....

....

....

....

0 2 4 6 8 10 12 14 16 18 20 22 24 26 28 30

Amount of Water Left (in ml)

Q3 Write down your types of paper in order of absorbency.

Most Absorbent

1. ....

2. ....

3. ....

4. ....

5. ....

Least Absorbent

Urn's paper didn't soak up much of the water.

The longer bars will be the less absorbent types of paper.

Graphs are great — more fun than biscuits...

The whole point of investigating things is to make conclusions (say what happened).
Drawing a graph can help make sense of the results — so it's easier to make conclusions.

MINI-PROJECT 2

Stretchy Tights

You know tights are stretchy — the question is, do they all
stretch the same amount, or are some tights more stretchy than others.

INVESTIGATION: Which is the most stretchy pair of tights?

1) Get some tights.
You need three or four pairs.

2) Label each pair so
they don't get mixed up.

3) Lay one pair of tights
out flat. Measure to find
out how long they are.

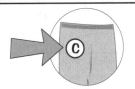
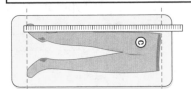

*Try to find tights that are about
the same length to start with.*

4) Put a weight
in one leg. I used
a tennis ball.

5) Hang the tights up,
and measure the leg
with the ball in.

*Keep your feet out of
the way or your toes
may get squashed!*

6) Do the same with
each pair of tights.

Q1   Here are some more instructions for the investigation.
Tick (✓) the ones which make it a better test.

☐ Always measure from
the waist to the toe.

☐ Use the same ball to test
each pair of tights.

☐ Do the investigation
on Tuesday.

☐ Wait for the ball to stop swinging
before you measure the length.

☐ Hang the tights very
close to the ground.

Now you know how to do the experiment, go and do it.
There's space on the next page to write down your results.

And s t r e t c h — and relax...

If tights weren't stretchy people wouldn't be able to get into them.
But the sixty-four thousand dollar question is — "Which tights are stretchiest?"...

Stretchy Tights

Do the experiment yourself, if you can.

Q1 **Write** down what weight you used in the tights.

....

You should have loads of stretchy results now. If not, use the spare results below.

Q2 **Write** your measurements in this table. Then **work out** how much each pair stretched.

Pair	Length BEFORE stretching	Length AFTER stretching	How much did the tights stretch?
A	cm	cm	cm
B	cm	cm	cm
C	cm	cm	cm
D	cm	cm	cm

Subtract this number   ...from this number   ...to get this number.

SPARE RESULTS
Pair A - before 91 cm, after 120 cm
Pair B - before 88 cm, after 105 cm
Pair C - before 95 cm, after 122 cm
Pair D - before 90 cm, after 114 cm

Q3 Finish this bar chart to show your results.

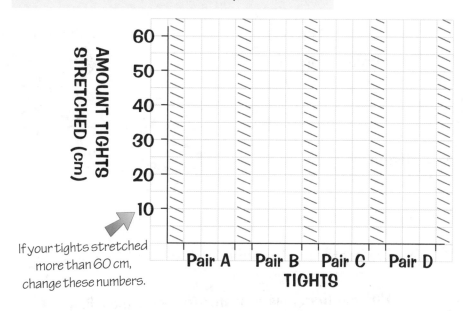

AMOUNT TIGHTS STRETCHED (cm)

If your tights stretched more than 60 cm, change these numbers.

Pair A   Pair B   Pair C   Pair D
TIGHTS

Bruce wasn't afraid to stand out from the crowd.

Q4 It's conclusion time. Just fill in the gaps.

The MOST STRETCHY tights were PAIR ....

The LEAST STRETCHY tights were PAIR ....

Stay cool — don't get your tights in a twist...

That's it — investigation complete. To find out which was the stretchiest pair of tights in the world, you would have to do the investigation on every single pair. Just imagine...

Testing Materials for a Purpose

Lots of things are made to be used for a certain job.
They have to be made of the right material for the job.

Humphrey Thinkalot is angry because nobody has invented
a floating armchair — so he's going to design it himself.

Q1 What properties does the armchair need to have? Tick (✓) the **two** right ones.

☐ It needs to float on water.

☐ It needs to wear away easily if it's rubbed.

☐ It needs to be transparent.

☐ It needs to be waterproof.

Humphrey has found a material to make the armchair from
— but he wants to compare it with other materials to make sure it's right for the job.

Q2 Humphrey wants to compare his material with other things that he
knows are waterproof. Circle the pictures of waterproof materials.

book

umbrella fabric

raincoat fabric

denim jeans

pottery plate

Q3 How should he test if they are **waterproof**? Write the best test on the dotted line.

Put the materials in water to see if they float.

Pour water onto the materials to see if they let it pass through.

Put them in the oven at gas mark 5 for 40 minutes.

Water fantastic page this is...

People have to test for properties of materials all the time.
If they didn't, they could end up inventing stuff like windows you can't see through...

Testing Materials for a Purpose

Most materials used in building things need to have more than one useful property.
For example, bricks are hard to scratch — and they are really strong too.

Q1 Now Humphrey needs to find out if his armchair will **float**.
What test should he do to find out? Write the answer on the dotted line.

....

....

Q2 Humphrey has made armchairs from lots of different materials. Now he wants to
find out which armchairs float. Tick (✓) the **two** things that will make his test fair.

☐ The armchairs should all be the same colour.

☐ The armchairs should all be the same size.

☐ The armchairs should all be the same shape.

☐ The armchairs should all smell the same.

Humphrey was in the
middle of the sea
when he remembered
about the oars.

Q3 Fill in the gaps in the sentences about testing materials, using words from the armchair.

MORE THAN
EXACTLY
ONE LOTS OF
PROPERTIES PEANUTS

When you test for the .... of a

material it's best to compare them with

.... other materials.

Materials usually need to have

.... one useful property.

Resting in my chair, water lapping at my feet...

Now you can invent anything you like — using materials that are right for the job.
Don't bother inventing the floating armchair though — it's a completely rubbish idea.

Revision Questions

It's time to find out what you remember about materials — on your marks, set, GO...

Q1 Fill in the table by ticking the properties for each material.
Say what the material is **usually** like. I've done the first one for you.

Rex loved chewing girders for breakfast.

Add an example of something you could make out of each material in the last column. I've done the first one for you.

	STRONG	WEAK	HARD	SOFT	STIFF	FLEXIBLE	NOT TRANSPARENT	TRANSPARENT	ROUGH	SMOOTH	ABSORBENT	EXAMPLE
wood	✓		✓		✓		✓			✓		Chair
glass												
metal												
plastic												
rubber												
cotton												
ceramic												
wool												

Q2 Which of these plastic things is strong and which is weak?
Write 'STRONG' or 'WEAK' after each picture.

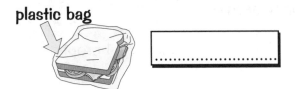

plastic bag ....

plastic slide ....

Anyone know a good material joke...?

Wow — would you look at the size of that table.

Revision Questions

Just what you wanted — another page jam-packed with tricky questions.

Q3   Imagine you are making the things in the black boxes. Answer the questions using materials and properties from the big table on p24 to help you.

I've done the first one for you.

table What material would you make it from? *wood* ....

Why would you use that material? *It's strong, hard, stiff*
.... *and smooth.* ....

window What material would you make it from? ....

Why would you use that material? ....

....

pin What material would you make it from? ....

Why would you use that material? ....

....

Q4   Fill in the blanks to say what property is being tested. Use 2 words from the box.

strength	hardness	flexibility	roughness

To test an object's .... we tried scratching it with a penknife.

To test an object's .... we measured how far we could bend it.

Q5   When you do an experiment, what should you do to make it a fair test? Tick the right answer.

> Testing, testing, one-two, one-two.

☐ Only change the thing you are testing and keep everything else the same.

☐ Change the thing you are testing and everything else.

Nope, nor do I...

That's all for materials folks... Oh, except for the index — which is a beauty.

Index